A Daily Quiet Time Guide and Journal

R. Clyde Hall, Jr.
Compiler

The Compiler

R. Clyde Hall, Jr. is supervisor, Youth Section, Church Training Department of The Sunday School Board.

Church Training Department
Sunday School Board, SBC
127 Ninth Avenue, North
Nashville, TN

Contents

The Compiler 2
How to Use Your *DiscipleHelps: A Daily Quiet Time Guide
and Journal* 4
Grasping God's Word 7

HEAR the Word
How to Use Worship Notes. 8
Worship Notes (13). 9

READ the Word
How to Have a Quiet Time 22
Quiet Time Diary (for 91 days) 25
How to Read the Bible Through. 71
Bible Reading Record 73

STUDY the Word
How to Use Bible Study Notes. 75
Bible Study Notes (13). 76
How to Do Advanced Bible Study. 89
Book Bible Study (3) 90

MEMORIZE the Word
How to Memorize Scripture. 93
Key Words for Scripture Memory 95
Scripture Verses to Memorize 96

MEDITATE on the Word
How to Pray. 97
Weekly Prayer Lists—Monday Through Sunday 100

DO the Word
How to Use Hearer's and Doer's and Witnessing Worksheets 107
Hearer's and Doer's Worksheet (3) 108
Person-to-Person Witnessing Plan Sheet 111

How to Use Your *DiscipleHelps: A Daily Quiet Time Guide and Journal*

DiscipleHelps is a tool to help you grow toward Christian maturity. As you come to know Jesus better each day, you will understand more fully what it means to make Him Lord of your life. By using this guide daily, you have a written record of what you are learning about God and what He wants you to do.

The Grasping God's Word explanation in the following paragraphs and the hand illustration on page 7 include the basic disciplines of the Christian life and the basic concept of evangelism in everyday life. Read the explanation each quarter in your new copy of the guide to help you focus on and apply these disciplines.

The six sections of this guide are pictured in the symbol of the hand on page 7: HEAR the Word; READ the Word; STUDY the Word; MEMORIZE the Word; MEDITATE on the Word; and DO the Word. Instructions for completing the activities are given in each section, and easy-to-use forms are provided.

Pages from this book may be removed and placed in your Bible if you do not want to take the guide with you. Holes have been punched so that the guide or individual pages can easily be placed in your *DiscipleYouth Notebook*. You may keep the guides in sequence by writing the dates used in the box outlined on the spine (bound edge) of each guide.

HEAR the Word *(Rom. 10:17)*

Hearing God's Word through sermons, lectures, testimonies, or in conversations is the first way you can begin to grasp God's Word. Yet listening requires concentration and effort on your part. You will forget most of what you hear—unless you write it down. Therefore, in order to remember more of what you hear, why not consider taking notes when you hear God's Word preached or taught? Writing down what is important to you dramatically increases your chances of remembering and heeding God's message. Forms for taking notes on thirteen worship services are included in this section.

READ the Word *(Rev. 1:3)*

Read God's Word daily during your quiet time. Studying, memorizing, and meditating all begin with reading. You have enough copies of the Quiet Time Diary for ninety-one days. A Bible Reading Record form is included to help you keep a record of what you have read. A completed record form indicates that you have read through the entire Bible.

STUDY the Word *(Acts 17:11)*

Grasping an object with three fingers is better than using two! Hearing God's Word in worship and reading God's Word in a daily quiet time will enable you to grasp God's Word fairly well. But to get an even stronger grasp, why not dig deeper into God's Word through personal and group study? Forms for thirteen Bible study sessions are included in this section. Use these forms with your Sunday School and/or Church Training lessons. Also provided for you to use are three advanced Bible study worksheets for Book Bible Study (one for each month). When you study God's Word, decide how you can apply it.

MEMORIZE the Word *(Ps. 119:11)*

Perhaps not your favorite! Yet so important! Instructions on how to memorize Scripture are given on pages 93-94. To help you make this memorizing activity a part of your quiet time, a place is provided to list each week's memory verse(s) under the date on each Quiet Time Diary worksheet. A circle has been placed in front of each verse or set of verses so that you can check if you have reviewed them. Ask God to lead you in sharing these verses with someone.

MEDITATE on the Word *(Ps. 1:2)*

Memorizing Scripture leads naturally to meditating on God's Word. As you go your way throughout the day, occasionally think about the verses. Seek to let the verses influence your attitudes and actions. In addition, you will use this section to go deeper in prayer. As you meditate, ask God what you need to do to apply these verses to your life.

Seven guides are included to help you remember to pray daily and in specific ways, with places to list your prayer requests and answers.

DO the Word *(Jas. 1:22)*

Jesus reminded us in *Luke 6:46-49* that we are to act on His words. James emphasized that we are to be *doers of the word, and not merely hearers who delude themselves (Jas. 1:22,* NASB). We are to evangelize other persons and disciple them. Three worksheets are provided (one for each month) along with one Person-to-Person Witnessing Plan Sheet. List on these forms some of the insights you have learned and indicate what you plan to do about those insights. See pages 108-111. The doing of the Word joins together the hearing, reading, studying, memorizing, and meditating, just as the palm joins the fingers of the hand as illustrated on page 7. Evangelism of non-Christians and encouragement of Christians are the proofs that God's Word has been put in our hearts.

* * * *

This guide, like any other tool, is effective only when used correctly. The basic disciplines of the Christian life are easier to develop when we are responsible to some other Christian. A DiscipleYouth group provides that kind of help. If no DiscipleYouth groups are in your church, ask a friend to use the guide also and then share with each other on a regular basis what God is doing in your lives. In addition, find opportunities to share each week with your youth group. Constantly apply to the situations in your life what you gain from God's Word.

Grasping God's Word

Anyone can pick up a Bible and hold it in his hand. However, you must work to get a firm grasp on God's Word in your heart. How do you get a good grasp on God's Word? Consider the hand in the illustration. To get a good, firm grasp on anything, you need to use all five fingers and then keep the object in the palm of your hand. Each finger of the hand illustration has a verse which identifies one way you can get a grasp on God's Word. Look up each verse and write the key word in that verse on the blank provided. God's Word is meant to be applied just as the hand is meant to be used.

How to Use Worship Notes

Thirteen Worship Notes forms are provided on the following pages—one for each week in the quarter. Use this form to write down anything the Lord seems to say to you in your heart during the morning and/or evening worship services. God may speak to you through songs, testimonies, and the preached Word. Expect God to speak to you! Then write down what He wants you to do, be, or know as you worship Him!

Worship Notes

Date:_____   Preacher:_____

Main Scripture:_____ Title (if any):_____

What I think God is saying to me through music, Scripture reading, testimony, or sermon:

Questions to ask, actions to do, attitudes to assume, or truths to believe:

Worship Notes

Date:_____   Preacher:_____

Main Scripture:_____   Title (if any):_____

What I think God is saying to me through music, Scripture reading, testimony, or sermon:

Questions to ask, actions to do, attitudes to assume, or truths to believe:

Worship Notes

Date:_____   Preacher:_____

Main Scripture:_____   Title (if any):_____

What I think God is saying to me through music, Scripture reading, testimony, or sermon:

Questions to ask, actions to do, attitudes to assume, or truths to believe:

Worship Notes

Date:_____   Preacher:_____

Main Scripture:_____   Title (if any):_____

What I think God is saying to me through music, Scripture reading, testimony, or sermon:

Questions to ask, actions to do, attitudes to assume, or truths to believe:

Worship Notes

Date:_____   Preacher:_____

Main Scripture:_____   Title (if any):_____

What I think God is saying to me through music, Scripture reading, testimony, or sermon:

Questions to ask, actions to do, attitudes to assume, or truths to believe:

Worship Notes

Date:_____   Preacher:_____

Main Scripture:_____   Title (if any):_____

What I think God is saying to me through music, Scripture reading, testimony, or sermon:

Questions to ask, actions to do, attitudes to assume, or truths to believe:

Worship Notes

Date:_____   Preacher:_____

Main Scripture:_____   Title (if any):_____

What I think God is saying to me through music, Scripture reading, testimony, or sermon:

Questions to ask, actions to do, attitudes to assume, or truths to believe:

Worship Notes

Date:_____   Preacher:_____

Main Scripture:_____   Title (if any):_____

What I think God is saying to me through music, Scripture reading, testimony, or sermon:

Questions to ask, actions to do, attitudes to assume, or truths to believe:

Worship Notes

Date:_____   Preacher:_____

Main Scripture:_____ Title (if any):_____

What I think God is saying to me through music, Scripture reading, testimony, or sermon:

Questions to ask, actions to do, attitudes to assume, or truths to believe:

Worship Notes

Date:_____   Preacher:_____

Main Scripture:_____   Title (if any):_____

What I think God is saying to me through music, Scripture reading, testimony, or sermon:

Questions to ask, actions to do, attitudes to assume, or truths to believe:

Worship Notes

Date:_____   Preacher:_____

Main Scripture:_____   Title (if any):_____

What I think God is saying to me through music, Scripture reading, testimony, or sermon:

Questions to ask, actions to do, attitudes to assume, or truths to believe:

Worship Notes

Date:_____   Preacher:_____

Main Scripture:_____ Title (if any):_____

What I think God is saying to me through music, Scripture reading, testimony, or sermon:

Questions to ask, actions to do, attitudes to assume, or truths to believe:

Worship Notes

Date:_____   Preacher:_____

Main Scripture:_____   Title (if any):_____

What I think God is saying to me through music, Scripture reading, testimony, or sermon:

Questions to ask, actions to do, attitudes to assume, or truths to believe:

How to Have a Quiet Time

When you commit your life to Jesus Christ, you begin a new relationship with Him. You become one of His children. You enter into a permanent relationship with God. This relationship with God enables you to have fellowship with Him. But fellowship has its ups and downs. Thus, although your relationship with God is constant, your fellowship with Him will vary with your availability to His leadership. A quiet time is a way of maintaining fellowship with God and evaluating your life-style. A quiet time is a way of building spiritual strength, becoming more sensitive to God's leadership, and applying His Word to your actions.

Two Essential Steps for Getting Started

STEP #1: Make a commitment to observe a daily quiet time.

Decide that your quiet time will be your first priority each day. Decide that each morning or evening you will avoid thoughts like, *After a while, I will have my quiet time. First, I must . . .*

STEP #2: Develop a plan for observing your daily quiet time.

Establish a regular schedule for your quiet time. Mark the time you will begin each day on the clock to your left.

What time will you need to go to bed to start your quiet time on time? Mark that time on the clock to your right.

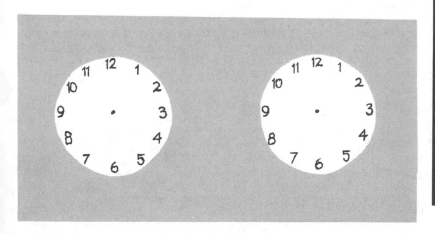

Decide where you will have your quiet time. You may choose a particular place in your room. When weather permits, you may want to go outdoors for your quiet time. Your quiet time place should be as free from distractions as possible. Choose a place where you can read your Bible and make notes..

My quiet time place will be _____

One Thing You Must Do If Your Quiet Time Is to Succeed

> KEEP ON KEEPING ON

If you miss lunch, do you quit eating altogether? Of course not! If you miss your quiet time one day, start again the next day.

If you have trouble getting up on time, analyze the problem. Are you going to bed early enough? Should you change some things about your daily schedule?

If you don't feel like getting out of bed, put one foot on the floor and go from there. Ask yourself, "If I stay in bed and miss my quiet time, how will I feel about it this afternoon? Tonight? Tomorrow?"

Realize that some quiet times will be more meaningful than others. Don't expect every quiet time to be an emotional high.

If possible, utilize one or two prayer partners to encourage you. Be honest with one another. Confess to one another when you miss a day. Support one another in prayer and discuss ways you can each be more consistent in having a quiet time.

Jesus spent time with His Heavenly Father, seeking fellowship, strength, and guidance. If God's Son needed to spend time with Him, how much more do you need to spend time with Him? Having a quiet time, you will become more like Christ as you follow His example and as you receive His power through prayer and the Word.

Quiet Time Diary

Date _____ Scripture _____

○ Memory verse of the week: _____

What God said to me:

What I said to God:

What I should do:

I could share these insights with _____ .

Date _____ Scripture _____

○ Memory verse of the week: _____

What God said to me:

What I said to God:

What I should do:

I could share these insights with _____.

Date _____ Scripture _____

○ Memory verse of the week: _____

What God said to me:

What I said to God:

What I should do:

I could share these insights with _____.

Date _____ Scripture _____
○ Memory verse of the week: _____

What God said to me:

What I said to God:

What I should do:

I could share these insights with _____.

Date _____ Scripture _____
○ Memory verse of the week: _____

What God said to me:

What I said to God:

What I should do:

I could share these insights with _____.

READ the Word

Date _____ Scripture _____

○ Memory verse of the week: _____

What God said to me:

What I said to God:

What I should do:

I could share these insights with _____.

Date _____ Scripture _____

○ Memory verse of the week: _____

What God said to me:

What I said to God:

What I should do:

I could share these insights with _____.

Date _____ Scripture _____

○ Memory verse of the week: _____

What God said to me:

What I said to God:

What I should do:

I could share these insights with _____.

Date _____ Scripture _____

○ Memory verse of the week: _____

What God said to me:

What I said to God:

What I should do:

I could share these insights with _____.

READ the Word

Date _____ Scripture _____

○ Memory verse of the week: _____

What God said to me:

What I said to God:

What I should do:

I could share these insights with _____.

Date _____ Scripture _____

○ Memory verse of the week: _____

What God said to me:

What I said to God:

What I should do:

I could share these insights with _____.

Date _____ Scripture _____

○ Memory verse of the week: _____

What God said to me:

What I said to God:

What I should do:

I could share these insights with _____.

Date _____ Scripture _____

○ Memory verse of the week: _____

What God said to me:

What I said to God:

What I should do:

I could share these insights with _____.

Date _____ Scripture _____
○ Memory verse of the week: _____

What God said to me:

What I said to God:

What I should do:

I could share these insights with _____.

Date _____ Scripture _____
○ Memory verse of the week: _____

What God said to me:

What I said to God:

What I should do:

I could share these insights with _____.

Date _____ Scripture _____

○ Memory verse of the week: _____

What God said to me:

What I said to God:

What I should do:

I could share these insights with _____.

Date _____ Scripture _____

○ Memory verse of the week: _____

What God said to me:

What I said to God:

What I should do:

I could share these insights with _____.

READ the Word

Date _____ Scripture _____

O Memory verse of the week: _____

What God said to me:

What I said to God:

What I should do:

I could share these insights with _____.

Date _____ Scripture _____

O Memory verse of the week: _____

What God said to me:

What I said to God:

What I should do:

I could share these insights with _____.

Date _____ Scripture _____

○ Memory verse of the week: _____

What God said to me:

What I said to God:

What I should do:

I could share these insights with _____.

Date _____ Scripture _____

○ Memory verse of the week: _____

What God said to me:

What I said to God:

What I should do:

I could share these insights with _____.

Date _____ Scripture _____

○ Memory verse of the week: _____

What God said to me:

What I said to God:

What I should do:

I could share these insights with _____.

Date _____ Scripture _____

○ Memory verse of the week: _____

What God said to me:

What I said to God:

What I should do:

I could share these insights with _____.

Date _____ Scripture _____

○ Memory verse of the week: _____

What God said to me:

What I said to God:

What I should do:

I could share these insights with _____.

Date _____ Scripture _____

○ Memory verse of the week: _____

What God said to me:

What I said to God:

What I should do:

I could share these insights with _____.

Date _____ Scripture _____

○ Memory verse of the week: _____

What God said to me:

What I said to God:

What I should do:

I could share these insights with _____.

Date _____ Scripture _____

○ Memory verse of the week: _____

What God said to me:

What I said to God:

What I should do:

I could share these insights with _____.

Date _____ Scripture _____
O Memory verse of the week: _____

What God said to me:

What I said to God:

What I should do:

I could share these insights with _____.

Date _____ Scripture _____
O Memory verse of the week: _____

What God said to me:

What I said to God:

What I should do:

I could share these insights with _____.

Date _____ Scripture _____
○ Memory verse of the week: _____

What God said to me:

What I said to God:

What I should do:

I could share these insights with _____.

Date _____ Scripture _____
○ Memory verse of the week: _____

What God said to me:

What I said to God:

What I should do:

I could share these insights with _____.

Date _____ Scripture _____

○ Memory verse of the week: _____

What God said to me:

What I said to God:

What I should do:

I could share these insights with _____.

Date _____ Scripture _____

○ Memory verse of the week: _____

What God said to me:

What I said to God:

What I should do:

I could share these insights with _____.

Date _____ Scripture _____
○ Memory verse of the week: _____

What God said to me:

What I said to God:

What I should do:

I could share these insights with _____.

Date _____ Scripture _____
○ Memory verse of the week: _____

What God said to me:

What I said to God:

What I should do:

I could share these insights with _____.

Date _____ Scripture _____

○ Memory verse of the week: _____

What God said to me:

What I said to God:

What I should do:

I could share these insights with _____.

Date _____ Scripture _____

○ Memory verse of the week: _____

What God said to me:

What I said to God:

What I should do:

I could share these insights with _____.

Date _____ Scripture _____

○ Memory verse of the week: _____

What God said to me:

What I said to God:

What I should do:

I could share these insights with _____.

Date _____ Scripture _____

○ Memory verse of the week: _____

What God said to me:

What I said to God:

What I should do:

I could share these insights with _____.

Date _____ Scripture _____

O Memory verse of the week: _____

What God said to me:

What I said to God:

What I should do:

I could share these insights with _____.

Date _____ Scripture _____

O Memory verse of the week: _____

What God said to me:

What I said to God:

What I should do:

I could share these insights with _____.

Date _____ Scripture _____

○ Memory verse of the week: _____

What God said to me:

What I said to God:

What I should do:

I could share these insights with _____.

Date _____ Scripture _____

○ Memory verse of the week: _____

What God said to me:

What I said to God:

What I should do:

I could share these insights with _____.

Date _____ Scripture _____

○ Memory verse of the week: _____

What God said to me:

What I said to God:

What I should do:

I could share these insights with _____.

Date _____ Scripture _____

○ Memory verse of the week: _____

What God said to me:

What I said to God:

What I should do:

I could share these insights with _____.

Date _____ Scripture _____

○ Memory verse of the week: _____

What God said to me:

What I said to God:

What I should do:

I could share these insights with _____.

Date _____ Scripture _____

○ Memory verse of the week: _____

What God said to me:

What I said to God:

What I should do:

I could share these insights with _____.

Date _____ Scripture _____

○ Memory verse of the week: _____

What God said to me:

What I said to God:

What I should do:

I could share these insights with _____.

Date _____ Scripture _____

○ Memory verse of the week: _____

What God said to me:

What I said to God:

What I should do:

I could share these insights with _____.

Date _____ Scripture _____

○ Memory verse of the week: _____

What God said to me:

What I said to God:

What I should do:

I could share these insights with _____.

Date _____ Scripture _____

○ Memory verse of the week: _____

What God said to me:

What I said to God:

What I should do:

I could share these insights with _____.

Date _____ Scripture _____

○ Memory verse of the week: _____

What God said to me:

What I said to God:

What I should do:

I could share these insights with _____.

Date _____ Scripture _____

○ Memory verse of the week: _____

What God said to me:

What I said to God:

What I should do:

I could share these insights with _____.

READ the Word

Date _____ Scripture _____
O Memory verse of the week: _____

What God said to me:

What I said to God:

What I should do:

I could share these insights with _____.

Date _____ Scripture _____
O Memory verse of the week: _____

What God said to me:

What I said to God:

What I should do:

I could share these insights with _____.

Date _____ Scripture _____

○ Memory verse of the week: _____

What God said to me:

What I said to God:

What I should do:

I could share these insights with _____.

Date _____ Scripture _____

○ Memory verse of the week: _____

What God said to me:

What I said to God:

What I should do:

I could share these insights with _____.

Date _____ Scripture _____

○ Memory verse of the week: _____

What God said to me:

What I said to God:

What I should do:

I could share these insights with _____.

Date _____ Scripture _____

○ Memory verse of the week: _____

What God said to me:

What I said to God:

What I should do:

I could share these insights with _____.

Date _____ Scripture _____

○ Memory verse of the week: _____

What God said to me:

What I said to God:

What I should do:

I could share these insights with _____.

Date _____ Scripture _____

○ Memory verse of the week: _____

What God said to me:

What I said to God:

What I should do:

I could share these insights with _____.

READ the Word

Date _____ Scripture _____
○ Memory verse of the week: _____

What God said to me:

What I said to God:

What I should do:

I could share these insights with _____.

Date _____ Scripture _____
○ Memory verse of the week: _____

What God said to me:

What I said to God:

What I should do:

I could share these insights with _____.

Date _____ Scripture _____
○ Memory verse of the week: _____

What God said to me:

What I said to God:

What I should do:

I could share these insights with _____ .

Date _____ Scripture _____
○ Memory verse of the week: _____

What God said to me:

What I said to God:

What I should do:

I could share these insights with _____ .

READ the Word

Date _____ Scripture _____

○ Memory verse of the week: _____

What God said to me:

What I said to God:

What I should do:

I could share these insights with _____.

Date _____ Scripture _____

○ Memory verse of the week: _____

What God said to me:

What I said to God:

What I should do:

I could share these insights with _____.

Date _____ Scripture _____
○ Memory verse of the week: _____

What God said to me:

What I said to God:

What I should do:

I could share these insights with _____.

Date _____ Scripture _____
○ Memory verse of the week: _____

What God said to me:

What I said to God:

What I should do:

I could share these insights with _____.

Date _____ Scripture _____

○ Memory verse of the week: _____

What God said to me:

What I said to God:

What I should do:

I could share these insights with _____.

Date _____ Scripture _____

○ Memory verse of the week: _____

What God said to me:

What I said to God:

What I should do:

I could share these insights with _____.

Date _____ Scripture _____

○ Memory verse of the week: _____

What God said to me:

What I said to God:

What I should do:

I could share these insights with _____.

Date _____ Scripture _____

○ Memory verse of the week: _____

What God said to me:

What I said to God:

What I should do:

I could share these insights with _____.

Date _____ Scripture _____

○ Memory verse of the week: _____

What God said to me:

What I said to God:

What I should do:

I could share these insights with _____.

Date _____ Scripture _____

○ Memory verse of the week: _____

What God said to me:

What I said to God:

What I should do:

I could share these insights with _____.

Date _____ Scripture _____
○ Memory verse of the week: _____

What God said to me:

What I said to God:

What I should do:

I could share these insights with _____.

Date _____ Scripture _____
○ Memory verse of the week: _____

What God said to me:

What I said to God:

What I should do:

I could share these insights with _____.

Date _____ Scripture _____

○ Memory verse of the week: _____

What God said to me:

What I said to God:

What I should do:

I could share these insights with _____.

Date _____ Scripture _____

○ Memory verse of the week: _____

What God said to me:

What I said to God:

What I should do:

I could share these insights with _____.

Date _____ Scripture _____

○ Memory verse of the week: _____

What God said to me:

What I said to God:

What I should do:

I could share these insights with _____ .

Date _____ Scripture _____

○ Memory verse of the week: _____

What God said to me:

What I said to God:

What I should do:

I could share these insights with _____ .

Date _____ Scripture _____

○ Memory verse of the week: _____

What God said to me:

What I said to God:

What I should do:

I could share these insights with _____.

Date _____ Scripture _____

○ Memory verse of the week: _____

What God said to me:

What I said to God:

What I should do:

I could share these insights with _____.

Date _____ Scripture _____

O Memory verse of the week: _____

What God said to me:

What I said to God:

What I should do:

I could share these insights with _____.

Date _____ Scripture _____

O Memory verse of the week: _____

What God said to me:

What I said to God:

What I should do:

I could share these insights with _____.

READ the Word

Date _____ Scripture _____

○ Memory verse of the week: _____

What God said to me:

What I said to God:

What I should do:

I could share these insights with _____.

Date _____ Scripture _____

○ Memory verse of the week: _____

What God said to me:

What I said to God:

What I should do:

I could share these insights with _____.

Date _____ Scripture _____

O Memory verse of the week: _____

What God said to me:

What I said to God:

What I should do:

I could share these insights with _____.

Date _____ Scripture _____

O Memory verse of the week: _____

What God said to me:

What I said to God:

What I should do:

I could share these insights with _____.

READ the Word

Date _____ Scripture _____

○ Memory verse of the week: _____

What God said to me:

What I said to God:

What I should do:

I could share these insights with _____.

Date _____ Scripture _____

○ Memory verse of the week: _____

What God said to me:

What I said to God:

What I should do:

I could share these insights with _____.

How to Read the
Bible Through

Reading the Bible through from *Genesis 1* to *Revelation 22* is not necessarily the best way to read this unique library. You would be a long time getting to the life and ministry of Jesus Christ as revealed in the Gospels. A balanced reading of the Bible calls for reading the Old and New Testaments simultaneously. Here are five approaches for reading through the Bible.

1. Place a bookmark in the Bible at three places: Genesis, Job, and Matthew. By reading one chapter from each of these sections every day, you will read the Old Testament once and the New Testament twice in about eighteen months.

2. Read one Bible chapter a day, and you will read the entire Bible in three years and three months.

3. Read three Bible chapters every weekday and five chapters on Sundays, and you will read the entire Bible in less than a year.

4. In January and February, read Genesis through Deuteronomy. In March and April, read all of the New Testament. In May and June, read Joshua through Esther. In July and August, read Job through Song of Solomon. In September and October, reread all of the New Testament. In November and December, read Isaiah through Malachi.

5. The weekly Bible reading plan on the next page will guide you in reading through the Old Testament once and the New Testament twice in one year. The youth devotional guide *encounter!* also carries outlines for Bible reading.

The Bible Reading Record on pages 73-74 will help you chart your progress in reading through the Bible.

Read the Bible Throughout Your Life

The reading and study of God's Word is a lifelong endeavor that never grows old. Once you have read the Bible through, read it again—in a different translation or Bible version. Choose different reading plans and schedules. Always keep a Bible reading notebook or journal so you can compare your notes and observations each time you read particular Bible books. Every time you read through God's Word, new and meaningful truths are brought to light.

The Bible holds the answer to humanity's past, present, and future. It is a wellspring of wisdom and divine instruction that never runs dry. Draw from this spring daily and find direction and purpose for your life.

52-Week Bible Reading Plan

1—Genesis 1—26
2—Genesis 27—50
3—Matthew
4—Mark
5—Exodus 1—21
6—Exodus 22—40
7—Luke
8—John
9—Leviticus
10—Acts
11—Numbers 1—18
12—Numbers 19—36
13—Romans; Galatians
14—1 & 2 Corinthians
15—Deuteronomy 1—17
16—Deuteronomy 18—34
17—Ephesians; Philippians;
   Colossians;
   1 & 2 Thessalonians;
   1 & 2 Timothy; Titus;
   Philemon
18—Hebrews; James;
   1 & 2 Peter
19—Joshua
20—1, 2, & 3 John; Jude;
   Revelation
21—Judges; Ruth
22—Job 1—31
23—Job 32—42; Ecclesiastes;
   Song of Solomon
24—1 Samuel
25—2 Samuel
26—Psalms 1—50
27—1 Kings
28—2 Kings

29—Psalms 51—100
30—1 Chronicles
31—2 Chronicles
32—Psalms 101—150
33—Ezra; Nehemiah; Esther
34—Proverbs
35—Matthew
36—Isaiah 1—35
37—Isaiah 36—66
38—Mark
39—Luke
40—Jeremiah 1—29
41—Jeremiah 30—52;
   Lamentations
42—John
43—Acts
44—Ezekiel 1—24
45—Ezekiel 25—48
46—Romans; Galatians
47—1 & 2 Corinthians
48—Daniel; Hosea; Joel; Amos
49—Ephesians; Philippians;
   Colossians;
   1 & 2 Thessalonians;
   1 & 2 Timothy; Titus;
   Philemon
50—Obadiah; Jonah; Micah;
   Nahum; Habakkuk;
   Zephaniah; Haggai;
   Zechariah; Malachi
51—Hebrews; James;
   1 & 2 Peter
52—1, 2, & 3 John; Jude;
   Revelation

Adapted from *Master Study Bible* (Nashville: Holman Bible Publishers, 1981), pp. 1597-1598.

BIBLE READING RECORD

When you have read a chapter, mark an X through the square. Beside each book write the date and year you finish reading it. You might keep a separate record of each translation you are reading. Use a different color for marking when you have read the chapter a second time. As you finish each book, ask God, "What do you want me to do with what I have read?"

Old Testament

Genesis	1	2	3	4	5	6	7	8	9	10	11	12	13	14	15	16	17	18	19	20
	21	22	23	24	25	26	27	28	29	30	31	32	33	34	35	36	37	38	39	40
	41	42	43	44	45	46	47	48	49	50										
Exodus	1	2	3	4	5	6	7	8	9	10	11	12	13	14	15	16	17	18	19	20
	21	22	23	24	25	26	27	28	29	30	31	32	33	34	35	36	37	38	39	40
Leviticus	1	2	3	4	5	6	7	8	9	10	11	12	13	14	15	16	17	18	19	20
	21	22	23	24	25	26	27													
Numbers	1	2	3	4	5	6	7	8	9	10	11	12	13	14	15	16	17	18	19	20
	21	22	23	24	25	26	27	28	29	30	31	32	33	34	35	36				
Deuteronomy	1	2	3	4	5	6	7	8	9	10	11	12	13	14	15	16	17	18	19	20
	21	22	23	24	25	26	27	28	29	30	31	32	33	34						
Joshua	1	2	3	4	5	6	7	8	9	10	11	12	13	14	15	16	17	18	19	20
	21	22	23	24																
Judges	1	2	3	4	5	6	7	8	9	10	11	12	13	14	15	16	17	18	19	20
	21																			
Ruth	1	2	3	4																
1 Samuel	1	2	3	4	5	6	7	8	9	10	11	12	13	14	15	16	17	18	19	20
	21	22	23	24	25	26	27	28	29	30	31									
2 Samuel	1	2	3	4	5	6	7	8	9	10	11	12	13	14	15	16	17	18	19	20
	21	22	23	24																
1 Kings	1	2	3	4	5	6	7	8	9	10	11	12	13	14	15	16	17	18	19	20
	21	22																		
2 Kings	1	2	3	4	5	6	7	8	9	10	11	12	13	14	15	16	17	18	19	20
	21	22	23	24	25															
1 Chronicles	1	2	3	4	5	6	7	8	9	10	11	12	13	14	15	16	17	18	19	20
	21	22	23	24	25	26	27	28	29											
2 Chronicles	1	2	3	4	5	6	7	8	9	10	11	12	13	14	15	16	17	18	19	20
	21	22	23	24	25	26	27	28	29	30	31	32	33	34	35	36				
Ezra	1	2	3	4	5	6	7	8	9	10										
Nehemiah	1	2	3	4	5	6	7	8	9	10	11	12	13							
Esther	1	2	3	4	5	6	7	8	9	10										
Job	1	2	3	4	5	6	7	8	9	10	11	12	13	14	15	16	17	18	19	20
	21	22	23	24	25	26	27	28	29	30	31	32	33	34	35	36	37	38	39	40
	41	42																		
Psalms	1	2	3	4	5	6	7	8	9	10	11	12	13	14	15	16	17	18	19	20
	21	22	23	24	25	26	27	28	29	30	31	32	33	34	35	36	37	38	39	40
	41	42	43	44	45	46	47	48	49	50	51	52	53	54	55	56	57	58	59	60
	61	62	63	64	65	66	67	68	69	70	71	72	73	74	75	76	77	78	79	80
	81	82	83	84	85	86	87	88	89	90	91	92	93	94	95	96	97	98	99	100
	101	102	103	104	105	106	107	108	109	110	111	112	113	114	115	116	117	118	119	120
	121	122	123	124	125	126	127	128	129	130	131	132	133	134	135	136	137	138	139	140
	141	142	143	144	145	146	147	148	149	150										
Proverbs	1	2	3	4	5	6	7	8	9	10	11	12	13	14	15	16	17	18	19	20
	21	22	23	24	25	26	27	28	29	30	31									
Ecclesiastes	1	2	3	4	5	6	7	8	9	10	11	12								
Song of Solomon	1	2	3	4	5	6	7	8												
Isaiah	1	2	3	4	5	6	7	8	9	10	11	12	13	14	15	16	17	18	19	20
	21	22	23	24	25	26	27	28	29	30	31	32	33	34	35	36	37	38	39	40
	41	42	43	44	45	46	47	48	49	50	51	52	53	54	55	56	57	58	59	60
	61	62	63	64	65	66														

READ the Word

Jeremiah	1	2	3	4	5	6	7	8	9	10	11	12	13	14	15	16	17	18	19	20
	21	22	23	24	25	26	27	28	29	30	31	32	33	34	35	36	37	38	39	40
	41	42	43	44	45	46	47	48	49	50	51	52								
Lamentations	1	2	3	4	5															
Ezekiel	1	2	3	4	5	6	7	8	9	10	11	12	13	14	15	16	17	18	19	20
	21	22	23	24	25	26	27	28	29	30	31	32	33	34	35	36	37	38	39	40
	41	42	43	44	45	46	47	48												
Daniel	1	2	3	4	5	6	7	8	9	10	11	12								
Hosea	1	2	3	4	5	6	7	8	9	10	11	12	13	14						
Joel	1	2	3																	
Amos	1	2	3	4	5	6	7	8	9											
Obadiah	1																			
Jonah	1	2	3	4																
Micah	1	2	3	4	5	6	7													
Nahum	1	2	3																	
Habakkuk	1	2	3																	
Zephaniah	1	2	3																	
Haggai	1	2																		
Zechariah	1	2	3	4	5	6	7	8	9	10	11	12	13	14						
Malachi	1	2	3	4																

New Testament

Matthew	1	2	3	4	5	6	7	8	9	10	11	12	13	14	15	16	17	18	19	20
	21	22	23	24	25	26	27	28												
Mark	1	2	3	4	5	6	7	8	9	10	11	12	13	14	15	16				
Luke	1	2	3	4	5	6	7	8	9	10	11	12	13	14	15	16	17	18	19	20
	21	22	23	24																
John	1	2	3	4	5	6	7	8	9	10	11	12	13	14	15	16	17	18	19	20
	21																			
Acts	1	2	3	4	5	6	7	8	9	10	11	12	13	14	15	16	17	18	19	20
	21	22	23	24	25	26	27	28												
Romans	1	2	3	4	5	6	7	8	9	10	11	12	13	14	15	16				
1 Corinthians	1	2	3	4	5	6	7	8	9	10	11	12	13	14	15	16				
2 Corinthians	1	2	3	4	5	6	7	8	9	10	11	12	13							
Galatians	1	2	3	4	5	6														
Ephesians	1	2	3	4	5	6														
Philippians	1	2	3	4																
Colossians	1	2	3	4																
1 Thessalonians	1	2	3	4	5															
2 Thessalonians	1	2	3																	
1 Timothy	1	2	3	4	5	6														
2 Timothy	1	2	3	4																
Titus	1	2	3																	
Philemon	1																			
Hebrews	1	2	3	4	5	6	7	8	9	10	11	12	13							
James	1	2	3	4	5															
1 Peter	1	2	3	4	5															
2 Peter	1	2	3																	
1 John	1	2	3	4	5															
2 John	1																			
3 John	1																			
Jude	1																			
Revelation	1	2	3	4	5	6	7	8	9	10	11	12	13	14	15	16	17	18	19	20
	21	22																		

How to Use Bible Study Notes

Use the Bible Study Notes forms that follow to prepare for Sunday School, Church Training, and other group Bible study experiences. Follow the simple suggestions on each worksheet. Make Sunday morning and evening Bible study lessons meaningful!

STUDY the Word

Bible Study Notes

For Sunday School, Church Training, retreats, and other group Bible study experiences. Here's how to get more . . .

Prepare personally (Check as you complete.)

☐ Pray for God's guidance for yourself and your leader.
☐ Read the Scripture from your Bible and record your thoughts below.
☐ Read your study piece and record your thoughts below and/or in spaces provided in your study piece.

Prepare biblically

Date:_____ Scripture passage:_____

Central or main truth:

Other truths:

Questions I have:

How I can apply this passage to life today:

Bring these notes to your next Bible study session.

Bible Study Notes

For Sunday School, Church Training, retreats, and other group Bible study experiences. Here's how to get more . . .

Prepare personally (Check as you complete.)

☐ Pray for God's guidance for yourself and your leader.
☐ Read the Scripture from your Bible and record your thoughts below.
☐ Read your study piece and record your thoughts below and/or in spaces provided in your study piece.

Prepare biblically

Date:_____ Scripture passage:_____

Central or main truth:

Other truths:

Questions I have:

How I can apply this passage to life today:

Bring these notes to your next Bible study session.

STUDY the Word

Bible Study Notes

For Sunday School, Church Training, retreats, and other group Bible study experiences. Here's how to get more . . .

Prepare personally (Check as you complete.)

☐ Pray for God's guidance for yourself and your leader.
☐ Read the Scripture from your Bible and record your thoughts below.
☐ Read your study piece and record your thoughts below and/or in spaces provided in your study piece.

Prepare biblically

Date:_____ Scripture passage:_____

Central or main truth:

Other truths:

Questions I have:

How I can apply this passage to life today:

Bring these notes to your next Bible study session.

Bible Study Notes

For Sunday School, Church Training, retreats, and other group Bible study experiences. Here's how to get more ...

Prepare personally (Check as you complete.)

- ☐ Pray for God's guidance for yourself and your leader.
- ☐ Read the Scripture from your Bible and record your thoughts below.
- ☐ Read your study piece and record your thoughts below and/or in spaces provided in your study piece.

Prepare biblically

Date:_____ Scripture passage:_____

Central or main truth:

Other truths:

Questions I have:

How I can apply this passage to life today:

Bring these notes to your next Bible study session.

Bible Study Notes

For Sunday School, Church Training, retreats, and other group Bible study experiences. Here's how to get more ...

Prepare personally (Check as you complete.)

☐ Pray for God's guidance for yourself and your leader.
☐ Read the Scripture from your Bible and record your thoughts below.
☐ Read your study piece and record your thoughts below and/or in spaces provided in your study piece.

Prepare biblically

Date:_____ Scripture passage:_____

Central or main truth:

Other truths:

Questions I have:

How I can apply this passage to life today:

Bring these notes to your next Bible study session.

Bible Study Notes

For Sunday School, Church Training, retreats, and other group Bible study experiences. Here's how to get more ...

Prepare personally (Check as you complete.)

☐ Pray for God's guidance for yourself and your leader.
☐ Read the Scripture from your Bible and record your thoughts below.
☐ Read your study piece and record your thoughts below and/or in spaces provided in your study piece.

Prepare biblically

Date:_____ Scripture passage:_____

Central or main truth:

Other truths:

Questions I have:

How I can apply this passage to life today:

Bring these notes to your next Bible study session.

STUDY the Word

Bible Study Notes

For Sunday School, Church Training, retreats, and other group Bible study experiences. Here's how to get more ...

Prepare personally (Check as you complete.)

☐ Pray for God's guidance for yourself and your leader.
☐ Read the Scripture from your Bible and record your thoughts below.
☐ Read your study piece and record your thoughts below and/or in spaces provided in your study piece.

Prepare biblically

Date:_____ Scripture passage:_____

Central or main truth:

Other truths:

Questions I have:

How I can apply this passage to life today:

Bring these notes to your next Bible study session.

Bible Study Notes

For Sunday School, Church Training, retreats, and other group Bible study experiences. Here's how to get more . . .

Prepare personally (Check as you complete.)

☐ Pray for God's guidance for yourself and your leader.
☐ Read the Scripture from your Bible and record your thoughts below.
☐ Read your study piece and record your thoughts below and/or in spaces provided in your study piece.

Prepare biblically

Date:_____ Scripture passage:_____

Central or main truth:

Other truths:

Questions I have:

How I can apply this passage to life today:

Bring these notes to your next Bible study session.

STUDY the Word

Bible Study Notes

For Sunday School, Church Training, retreats, and other group Bible study experiences. Here's how to get more . . .

Prepare personally (Check as you complete.)

☐ Pray for God's guidance for yourself and your leader.
☐ Read the Scripture from your Bible and record your thoughts below.
☐ Read your study piece and record your thoughts below and/or in spaces provided in your study piece.

Prepare biblically

Date:_____ Scripture passage:_____

Central or main truth:

Other truths:

Questions I have:

How I can apply this passage to life today:

Bring these notes to your next Bible study session.

Bible Study Notes

For Sunday School, Church Training, retreats, and other group Bible study experiences. Here's how to get more . . .

Prepare personally (Check as you complete.)

☐ Pray for God's guidance for yourself and your leader.
☐ Read the Scripture from your Bible and record your thoughts below.
☐ Read your study piece and record your thoughts below and/or in spaces provided in your study piece.

Prepare biblically

Date:_____ Scripture passage:_____

Central or main truth:

Other truths:

Questions I have:

How I can apply this passage to life today:

Bring these notes to your next Bible study session.

STUDY the Word

Bible Study Notes

For Sunday School, Church Training, retreats, and other group Bible study experiences. Here's how to get more ...

Prepare personally (Check as you complete.)

☐ Pray for God's guidance for yourself and your leader.
☐ Read the Scripture from your Bible and record your thoughts below.
☐ Read your study piece and record your thoughts below and/or in spaces provided in your study piece.

Prepare biblically

Date:_____ Scripture passage:_____

Central or main truth:

Other truths:

Questions I have:

How I can apply this passage to life today:

Bring these notes to your next Bible study session.

Bible Study Notes

For Sunday School, Church Training, retreats, and other group Bible study experiences. Here's how to get more ...

Prepare personally (Check as you complete.)

☐ Pray for God's guidance for yourself and your leader.
☐ Read the Scripture from your Bible and record your thoughts below.
☐ Read your study piece and record your thoughts below and/or in spaces provided in your study piece.

Prepare biblically

Date:_____ Scripture passage:_____

Central or main truth:

Other truths:

Questions I have:

How I can apply this passage to life today:

Bring these notes to your next Bible study session.

Bible Study Notes

For Sunday School, Church Training, retreats, and other group Bible study experiences. Here's how to get more . . .

Prepare personally (Check as you complete.)

☐ Pray for God's guidance for yourself and your leader.
☐ Read the Scripture from your Bible and record your thoughts below.
☐ Read your study piece and record your thoughts below and/or in spaces provided in your study piece.

Prepare biblically

Date:_____ Scripture passage:_____

Central or main truth:

Other truths:

Questions I have:

How I can apply this passage to life today:

Bring these notes to your next Bible study session.

How to Do Advanced Bible Study

Expand your Bible study experience to include a book study each month. Use the worksheets on pages 90-92 to guide your study and to record information about the book selected. For additional types of advanced Bible study and worksheets, see *DiscipleYouth Notebook*, pp. 41-54.

A Plan

As you make plans to do book Bible study, consider the following books in this order:

New Testament.—John; Luke; Acts; 1 and 2 Timothy; Titus; Philemon; 1 and 2 Thessalonians; 1 and 2 Corinthians; Galatians; Ephesians; Philippians; Colossians; Romans; Matthew; Mark.

Old Testament.—Psalms; Genesis; Exodus; Joshua; Judges; 1 and 2 Samuel; 1 Kings; 2 Chronicles; 2 Kings; Amos; Hosea; Micah; Jeremiah; Ezekiel; Jonah; Isaiah; Ezra; Nehemiah.

Tools Needed

If you are going to dig, you will do a better job if you have some tools, like:

1. *A good Bible.*—You will do better Bible study if you have a recent translation, like *DiscipleYouth Bible* (NASB), *Good News Bible* (GNB), *The New International Version* (NIV), or Revised Standard Version (RSV). *The Living Bible* (TLB) is a paraphrase of the Bible and is good for rapid reading of large sections of the Bible or for comparing with Bible translations. Many Bibles have references in the page margins. These letters or numbers help you locate other verses which relate to the verse you are reading.

2. *A concordance.*—A concordance is simply an alphabetical listing of the words used in a particular translation of the Bible. Your Bible may have a concordance in the back.

3. *A Bible dictionary.*—A Bible dictionary defines words, places, persons, and subjects found in the Bible.

4. *A Bible commentary.*—In a commentary a writer simply tries to explain or comment on a certain passage or book. Your pupil's books or leaflets in Sunday School and Church Training are simply commentaries written for you and other youth your age to help you understand the Bible better.

STUDY the Word

Book Bible Study

The books of the Bible were written by *real* persons to *real* people with *real* problems. By studying one book of the Bible at a time, you can interpret verses and passages in their historical contexts and draw out principles for Christian living today. Here are some steps to take:

1. Rapidly read the entire book. As you read, jot down responses to the following questions:

What kind of literature is it? Circle one or more: history, poetry, drama, gospel-biography, letter, apocalyptic, law, prophecy.

What are some major ideas presented in this book?

2. Using your Bible commentary, dictionary, or pupil's or teacher's book, write down answers to these questions:

Who wrote the book?

When was the book written?

What caused the writer to write the book?

What are the major themes of the book?

How does this book speak to living the Christian life today?

Book Bible Study

The books of the Bible were written by *real* persons to *real* people with *real* problems. By studying one book of the Bible at a time, you can interpret verses and passages in their historical contexts and draw out principles for Christian living today. Here are some steps to take:

1. Rapidly read the book in its entirety. As you read, jot down responses to the following questions:

What kind of literature is it? Circle one or more: history, poetry, drama, gospel-biography, letter, apocalyptic, law, prophecy.

What are some major ideas presented in this book?

2. Using your Bible commentary, dictionary, or pupil's or teacher's book, write down answers to these questions:

Who wrote the book?

When was the book written?

What caused the writer to write the book?

What were the major themes of the book?

How does this book speak to living the Christian life today?

Book Bible Study

The books of the Bible were written by *real* persons to *real* people with *real* problems. By studying one book of the Bible at a time, you can interpret verses and passages in their historical contexts and draw out principles for Christian living today. Here are some steps to take:

1. Rapidly read the book in its entirety. As you read, jot down responses to the following questions:

What kind of literature is it? Circle one or more: history, poetry, drama, gospel-biography, letter, apocalyptic, law, prophecy.

What are some major ideas presented in this book?

2. Using your Bible commentary, dictionary, or pupil's or teacher's book, write down answers to these questions:

Who wrote the book?

When was the book written?

What caused the writer to write the book?

What were the major themes of the book?

How does this book speak to living the Christian life today?

How to Memorize Scripture

Most folks try to excuse themselves from the discipline of memorizing Scripture by saying, "I just can't memorize." Yet God promises some exciting things for those disciples who memorize His Word! The guidelines that follow are designed to help you in Scripture memory.

STEP ONE: Pray About Memorizing God's Word

Commit your will to His will! God's will for all disciples is to remember His Word *(Deut. 6:6,7; Ps. 119:11,16,73)*. The Lord gives you a tremendous promise in *Philippians 4:13—I can do all things through Him who strengthens me* (NASB). Does the *all things* in this verse include Scripture memory? _____ If you believe it does and you believe it is God's will for you to memorize Scripture, why not right now surrender your mind and will to God? Trust the Lord to enable you to remember His Word!

STEP TWO: Follow a Scripture Memory Plan

Set your own goal: either one or two verses per week.

STEP THREE: Choose Verses to Memorize

Here are some different ways to select verses to memorize:

1. Follow the weekly assignments in your *DiscipleYouth Notebooks.* You have Scripture Memory Cards with the verses, topics, and references printed on them. Put these cards in your pocket or purse. Use these cards throughout your day during spare time. Continue working with these verses until you have them all memorized. (ACTEENS: Use this to help learn verses for *Studiact: Acteens Individual Achievement Plan.*).

2. When you see the "Memory Bug" in your Sunday School pupil's book or leaflet, write your own memory cards with topics, references, and verses. Memorize one or two of these "Memory Bug" verses every week.

3. As you have your quiet time, you will discover other verses you will want to memorize. Create memory cards for these meaningful verses.

4. Ask your youth leader, youth minister, or pastor to help you find verses to memorize. See suggestions on page 96.

STEP FOUR: Consider a Few Practical Suggestions

1. Use the awesome power of your SUBCONSCIOUS mind! Sounds scary, right? Try this: Quote your verse (with its topic and reference, of course) the last thing before you go to sleep at night. Literally sleep on it! Then quote your verse again when you wake up in the morning. Make God's Word your first word in the morning and your last word at night. You will be surprised how easy memory work becomes.

2. As you memorize verses, try to associate the words with VISUAL objects.

3. As you review your verses, try to WRITE them down.

4. If you like MUSIC, why not create a tune to help you remember verses or see *DiscipleYouth Songs.*

5. Finally, RELAX. If you fall behind in Scripture memory, don't quit altogether. Pick up where you left off, review, and start all over again.

Spend time, work, and review. Follow the practical suggestions on the chart below:

KEY WORDS FOR SCRIPTURE MEMORY

Time

1. Use three minutes of your daily quiet time Bible study each morning for Scripture memorization.
2. Spend five minutes working on verses just before bedtime.
3. Use spare time for Scripture memorization.

Work

1. Study the context.
2. Think through the verse.
3. Read it aloud several times.
4. Memorize the topic and quote the Scripture reference before and after the verse.
5. Memorize bits and phrases.
6. Connect clauses as you go.
7. Learn the verse word perfect.
8. Meditate on the verse all day.
9. Apply the verse as you go.

Review

1. Review the verses learned for five weeks or thirty days.
2. This means your maximum number of verses on any given day will be twelve—reviewing eleven and working on the one new verse.
3. After a person has reviewed a verse thirty times, he should review it once or twice a month.

Scripture Verses To Memorize

DiscipleYouth Notebook
Psalm 119:11
Isaiah 53:6
Matthew 28:6
John 1:12
John 14:15
Acts 2:42
Acts 3:19
Romans 12:1-2
Romans 14:9
Hebrews 4:12
Hebrews 4:16
1 Peter 2:24
1 John 1:9
1 John 4:15
1 John 5:11
Revelation 3:20

DiscipleYouth II Notebook
1 John 4:7-8
Matthew 5:16
Psalm 56:3
1 Timothy 4:12
Hebrews 12:3
1 Peter 3:15
1 Peter 4:14
1 Corinthians 9:22
Hebrews 10:24-25
1 Corinthians 12:4-7
Ephesians 4:11-12
1 John 3:18

Roman Road to Salvation
Romans 3:23
Romans 6:23
Romans 5:8
Romans 10:9-10
Romans 10:13

Survival Kit
Psalm 119:11
Matthew 28:18-20
Romans 5:10
Romans 12:4-5
1 Corinthians 2:14
Galatians 5:22-23
Philippians 1:6
Philippians 4:6
Colossians 3:8-10
2 Timothy 3:16
1 Peter 4:10

Survival Kit 2
Ephesians 4:11-12
Luke 22:27
Ecclesiastes 6:12
Psalm 12:3-4
Luke 12:15
Matthew 6:19-21
Philippians 4:19
1 Corinthians 10:26
Matthew 18:15
1 Corinthians 11:31-32
Luke 12:37
John 4:34-35
Ephesians 4:15-16
Ephesians 5:1-2
Mark 9:35
Matthew 18:3
1 Timothy 6:6-8
2 Peter 3:9-10
Hebrews 13:15-16
1 Samuel 3:10
1 Corinthians 3:16-17
Deuteronomy 15:17

Jesus commands us in *Matthew 28:18-20* to go and make disciples. Evangelism and discipleship go together. Going is a result of receiving God's Word. And the power to go comes from making God's Word a vital part of our lives. Memorize God's Word. Then do God's Word by letting His Word be a lamp to your feet.

How to Pray

To talk with God you must believe that He is present even though you cannot see Him as you see your parents and friends (*Heb. 11:6*). Faith is not *hoping* that God will listen and speak with you but *trusting* that He is real and available for conversation.

God speaks through His written Word. He speaks through Christian leaders and friends. He sometimes speaks powerfully from a quiet voice in your heart. Prayer is not only talking to God, but also listening for His voice.

How to Avoid a Bad Connection

Check your relationships, your attitudes, and your motivation. If your prayer life is being weakened by a problem in one of these areas, pray about that problem and correct it with God's help. Keep on growing!

Checklist for a Stimulating Conversation

PART 1: LISTENING TO GOD

Begin your quiet time by reading a passage of Scripture. Read the daily passage prayerfully, asking God to speak to you as you read it.

As you read the passage, ask the Lord to call to your attention any—

example to follow,
command to obey,
error to avoid,
sin to forsake,
promise to claim,
new thought about Himself.

Use the Quiet Time Diary to keep a record of the insights you gain as God speaks to you through His Word.

PART 2: TALKING TO GOD

As you talk to God each day, be sure your conversation covers these five areas: praise, confession, thanksgiving, petition, intercession.

A. Praise

Praise is closely related to thanksgiving, but there is a difference. Praise is adoring God for who He is. Thanksgiving is thanking God for what He has done. Praise is showing love to God; thanksgiving is expressing gratitude. God is to be praised for His character. He is to be thanked for His actions.

Begin your prayer by praising God. For example, "I love You, God. I praise You for being who You are."

B. Confession

(1) Ask the Lord to make you aware of any sins which are hurting your fellowship with Him.
(2) Confess each sin individually to the Lord.
(3) Agree with God that the sin is wrong.
(4) Express your desire to avoid these sins in the future.
(5) Claim by faith His forgiveness.
(6) Right the wrong to whatever extent you can.
(7) Accept by faith the fact that you are totally cleansed (*1 John 1:9*).

C. Thanksgiving

(1) Express your thankfulness for specific things.
(2) Cultivate a general attitude of thankfulness whatever the circumstances (*1 Thess. 5:18*).

D. Petition—Praying for Yourself
  (1) Pray for spiritual growth.
  (2) Pray for your material needs.
  (3) Share with God the desires of your heart and trust Him to respond in the best possible way.

E. Intercession—Prayer for Others
  Pray for the needs of other people. In your mind draw together God and the person in need. God's grace will meet the needs of that person.
  Be willing to act on your prayers. If you ask God to help you in history class, act on your prayer by studying as you should. If you pray that a friend will recover from grief over a relative who has died, be willing to share words of encouragement and deeds of love with that friend.

Using Prayer Lists and Daily Prayer Guide
  On a separate piece of paper, prepare your Daily Prayer Guide. Include the five areas discussed on pages 98-99: Praise, Confession, Thanksgiving, Petition, and Intercession (or use page 33 in your *Disciple Youth Notebook*). Follow this guide to keep a record of your daily conversation with God.
  The seven weekly prayer lists provide a guide and a record of weekly prayers for others and for tasks God wants you to accomplish. Using these lists you will be able to focus your prayers on a particular group or area of need each day of the week:
  Monday—Missionaries
  Tuesday—Tasks God wants you to achieve
  Wednesday—Workers in the kingdom of God
  Thursday—Those in authority over us
  Friday—Family and friends
  Saturday—Sinners who are lost
  Sunday—Sunday services

MEDITATE on the Word

Weekly Prayer Lists

Monday: Missionaries

MONDAY: "M" is for missionaries. Do your best to meet your missionaries. To know them will give you a personal touch. Of course, you don't have to know a person to pray for him. Use the various materials that contain the list of missionaries for whom you can pray on their birthdays. Some are *Accent, encounter! Open Windows,* and *Probe.* Do not allow missions to become just a program, with a necessary task, which does not touch you in a personal way.

DATE	MISSIONARY	SPECIFIC REQUEST	ANSWER

Tuesday: Tasks

TUESDAY: "T" is for TASKS God wants you to achieve. Every year a person should set out some goals he feels God would have him achieve. For instance your goals this year might include:
1. Have a time alone with God daily.
2. Memorize two Scripture verses per week.
3. Memorize one poem a week.
4. Read one book every two weeks.
5. Cultivate lost neighbors for Christ.

Praying every Tuesday that God will help you achieve these tasks will reset the goals in your mind. If you should fall behind in your achievements, your Tuesday prayer list will push you forward again.

DATE	TASK GOD WANTS ME TO DO	PROGRESS

MEDITATE on the Word

Wednesday: Workers

WEDNESDAY: "W" is for the workers for the Kingdom. *The harvest truly is great, but the labourers are few: pray ye therefore the Lord of the harvest, that he would send forth labourers into his harvest (Luke 10:2).* God wants us to pray for pastors, Sunday School teachers, church staff people, deacons, committee members, Church Training leaders, WMU and Baptist Men's workers.

Pray also that *God would raise up young people who would be leaders for Christ among other young people.*

DATE	WORKER	SPECIFIC REQUEST	ANSWER

Thursday: Leaders

THURSDAY; "T" is for those in authority over us. *First Timothy 2:1-2 states, First of all, then I urge that entreaties and prayer, petitions and thanksgivings, be made on behalf of all men, for kings and all who are in authority, in order that we may lead a tranquil and quiet life in all godliness and dignity* (NASB). So often we complain about the poor performance of those who serve in elected office. Has it dawned on you that the elected officials would do better if we followed the command to pray for them?

```
S  R
P  E    1. For men and women who will lead us into a time of
E  Q       godliness, tranquility, and dignity
C  U    2. For election of such people
I  E    3. For our leaders to have wisdom to know the right, and
A  S       courage to do it
L  T    4. That Christians in office will not embarrass the church
   S
```

Some for whom you would want to pray are:

United States President   School Board Member
United States Senator   City Councilman
United States Congressman   Chief of Police
State Governor   City Mayor
State Representative   Judges

DATE	OFFICIAL	SPECIAL REQUEST	ANSWER

MEDITATE on the Word

Friday: Family and Friends

FRIDAY: "F" is for family and friends. Paul suggested to his young friend Timothy that he remember him in prayer both night and day (*2 Tim. 1:3*). Jesus prayed for His disciples (*John 17*). God wants us to pray sincerely for friends and family. A good day for special remembrance of family and friends is Friday.

DATE	NAME	SPECIAL REQUEST	ANSWER

Saturday: Sinners

SATURDAY: "S" is for sinners who are lost. In praying for the lost, pray that the Holy Spirit will open and enlighten their eyes. Because the lost person is blinded by Satan *(2 Cor. 4:4)*, you should pray that Satan's power over the lost would be broken. Next, pray for God to send Christians to witness to the lost person *(Acts 8:26)*. Finally, pray that the lost will bend their wills to Jesus Christ until Christ is received as Lord and Savior.

The other day a young person said, "I don't need to pray for the lost so much as I need to pray for myself that I will have the courage to witness." Well spoken! The reason you don't talk to young people about God is because you are not talking to God about young people. Pray that God will burden your heart for your lost friends until you are constantly aware of their utter dependence on you. Pray that He will help you to develop skill and tact in witnessing. Pray every day until God moves you to share Christ.

DATE	NAME	SPECIFIC REQUEST	ANSWER

MEDITATE on the Word

Sunday: Services

SUNDAY: "S" is for Sunday services. The response to the invitation will be in proportion to the visitation and prayer that precede the Sunday services. No prayer—no results! Much prayer—great results! On Sunday morning and evening ask God to manifest Himself in wonderful power. Pray that the Holy Spirit will bless the Sunday School teacher's lesson, the pastor's sermon, and the Church Training sessions. Petition the Father for a true worship of Him during all the church services.

DATE	SPECIAL REQUEST	ANSWER

How to Use Hearer's and Doer's and Witnessing Worksheets

Sometime during the last week of each month in the quarter, complete one of the Hearer's and Doer's Worksheets. These worksheets record several plans of action for including disciplemaking and evangelism in the Christian life.

Use the Person-to-Person Witnessing Plan Sheet to record the names of non-Christian friends, along with some information about them. Pray that God will give you the words to say and guide your actions as you get involved in the lives of these persons. Share with them what Jesus is doing in your life and explain how they can accept Him as their personal Lord and Savior.

Hearer's and Doer's Worksheet

Personal Preparations

What God is telling me about an area of my life I need to work on:

What I am telling God about specific things I can do to improve:

Witness Training

What God is telling me to tell others:

Persons to tell (names):

Witness Experiences

Actions to take to share with a non-Christian:

Spiritual Development

Actions to take to share with another Christian:

Hearer's and Doer's Worksheet

Personal Preparations

What God is telling me about an area of my life I need to work on:

What I am telling God about specific things I can do to improve:

Witness Training

What God is telling me to tell others:

Persons to tell (names):

Witness Experiences

Actions to take to share with a non-Christian:

Spiritual Development

Actions to take to share with another Christian:

DO the Word

Hearer's and Doer's Worksheet

Personal Preparations

What God is telling me about an area of my life I need to work on:

What I am telling God about specific things I can do to improve:

Witness Training

What God is telling me to tell others:

Persons to tell (names):

Witness Experiences

Actions to take to share with a non-Christian:

Spiritual Development

Actions to take to share with another Christian:

Person-to-Person Witnessing Plan Sheet

Name of the non-Christian Friend: _____

Address: _____

Phone: _____ Age: _____ Sex: _____

School: _____

Interests/Hobbies: _____

Special Needs (Spiritual, Mental, Social, Emotional,

   Physical): _____

PLAN	RESPONSE
1. Win their friendship.	
2. Spend time with them.	
3. Express love to them.	
4. Listen.	
5. Share.	

DO the Word

This *DiscipleHelps: A Daily Quiet Time Guide and Journal* is a companion to DiscipleYouth and DiscipleYouth II. However, it also is designed to be used by youth not yet involved in DiscipleYouth. The contents reflect the DiscipleYouth training process. DiscipleYouth can be completed through four approaches: individual, one-to-one, small group—notebook only, and small group with notebook and additional resources.

DiscipleYouth is an in-depth discipleship-evangelism training process for youth in grades 7-12. DiscipleYouth and DiscipleYouth II are comprehensive expressions of the National Youth Discipleship/Evangelism Strategy. Through the four levels of the strategy—Personal Preparation, Witness Training, Witness Experience, and Spiritual Development—youth will:

- Examine the meaning of discipleship.
- Realize that all areas of their lives belong to God.
- Begin to practice a witnessing life-style.
- Begin a regular quiet time of systematic Bible study, prayer, and Scripture memorization.
- Learn to apply spiritual growth to ministry needs and gain personal witness experience.
- Become more involved in and supportive of ongoing program emphases of their local congregation.
- Share the basics of Christian growth with new Christians.

DiscipleYouth materials are available through the Baptist Book Stores and Materials Services Department, 127 Ninth Avenue, North, Nashville, Tennessee 37234.